WHO AM I?

Ella L. Winn

Trilogy Christian Publishers
A Wholly Owned Subsidiary of Trinity Broadcasting Network
2442 Michelle Drive
Tustin, CA 92780

Cover design by: Cornerstone Creative Solutions

For information, address Trilogy Christian Publishing
Rights Department, 2442 Michelle Drive, Tustin, Ca 92780.
Trilogy Christian Publishing/ TBN and colophon are trademarks of Trinity Broadcasting Network.

For information about special discounts for bulk purchases, please contact Trilogy Christian Publishing.

Manufactured in the United States of America

10 9 8 7 6 5 4 3 2 1

Library of Congress Cataloging-in-Publication Data is available.

ISBN 978-1-68556-271-7 (Print Book)
ISBN 978-1-68556-270-0 (ebook)

Contents

Book One

It was the first day of summer.

Chloe awoke from sleep. As she combed her hair, brushed her teeth, and put her clothes on, she looked in the mirror and said, "Who am I?"

Chloe went downstairs to eat breakfast with her mom, baby sister, and their dog Sally. Chloe looked at her mom and then at her sister and said, "Who am I?"

Mom said, "You are my daughter, and your father and I love you very much. You are also a big sister."

After breakfast, Chloe went outside to play with her friend Janet, who lived next door. Chloe and Janet played until it was time for lunch.

Chloe looked at Janet and said, "Who am I?"

Janet said, "You are my best friend!"

Chloe went to visit her grandparents, who lived in the next town. Chloe loved to go visit them. They would always have brownies and milk waiting for her and her sister.

Grandma Ann was sitting in a chair on the porch peeling peas. As she peeled the peas, she sang a song, which was soft and sweet.

Chloe looked at her grandmother and said, "Who am I?"

Grandmother paused and said, "For you are my granddaughter who is incredibly special to me, and I love you."

When Chloe returned home, she asked her mother if it was alright to ride her bike up and down the sidewalk. Mom said, "Yes, you may be careful, and remember dinner will be ready soon."

Chloe rode her bike up and down the sidewalk. As she rode, she would say, "Who am I?"

Chloe's mother was busy preparing dinner for the family. When she had finished, she set the table and called Chloe inside to wash up and eat dinner. By this time, her father had come home from work.

Everyone sits down to eat and talk about their day. Mom said she went to visit the neighbor two houses down the street, who had been sick but is better now. She made soup and carried it to her. Dad said he had a good day at work, and he was able to witness to a co-worker the love of Jesus.

Chloe looked around and thought about what had happened during her day and what she could say. Then she said, "Who am I?"

Dad said, "Who am I?"

Chloe said, "Yes, who am I?"

Her father said, "For you are my daughter."

Chloe said, "Yes, Dad, this is true. I have friends; Mom said that she loves me, Grandma said that I am her granddaughter, and guess what, I am a big sister."

A big smile appeared on Chloe's face as she said, "A lot of people love me. Jesus loves me."

Chloe got ready for bed. Her mother came to tuck her in along with dad and to make sure she said her prayers.

"Do you remember your mother and me telling you that God loves you? According to Psalm 139:14, God loves you so much that there is only one like you. You are fearfully and wonderfully made by the hands of God. Your blood type is like no other. You have a special and unique family. God loves and cares for you so much that He knows the number of hairs that are on your head. This is in Matthew 10:30."

"Really, Dad?!" said Chloe.

"Really," said Dad.

Chloe prayed by saying, "Lord, I thank You for today. Thank You for Mom and Dad, my sister, Mary, my grandparents, and my best friend, Janet. I thank You that I am loved by my family and I am loved by You."

Who Am I? Book One Scriptures

"I will praise You, for I am fearfully *and* wonderfully made; Marvelous are Your works, And *that* my soul knows very well" (Psalm 139:14, NKJV).

"But the very hairs of your head are all numbered" (Matthew 10:30, NKJV).

"But the very hairs of your head are all numbered. Do not fear therefore; you are of more value than many sparrows" (Luke 12:7, NKJV).

Parents, grandparents, aunts, or uncles, as you read this book to your precious little ones. You will be filled with the peace of God. For your little ones will be encouraged and strengthened by the Word of God as it pertains to the young children of God.

There are many questions in the world today that we seek answers to.

In *Who Am I?* you will meet Chloe and Mark, who has many questions that need to be addressed.

Will they find the answers they are looking for? Take this journey with them to find out.

Ella L. Winn is the second child of four children. She was born in Shreveport, Louisiana, and raised in Coushatta, Louisiana, where she currently resides. Ella is a minister, author, sister, aunt, and godmother of many children.

As an active member of House of Refuge Full Gospel Ministries, Ella serves as secretary and intercessor. Ella is a kingdom builder and is eager to help in any way necessary.

Ella has been an educator for over twenty-one years and loves working with young children. Ella's favorite saying is "Trust God in all things." According to Psalm 62:8, "All you people Trust in him at all times."

CPSIA information can be obtained
at www.ICGtesting.com
Printed in the USA
BVHW011216090223
658199BV00017B/341

WHO AM I?
Ella L. Winn

Contents

Book Two

Mark lives with his father, mother, two sisters, and three brothers. Mark was the youngest of the children. Sometimes he feels left out of the family because he is so small. There are some things he's just not big enough to do, like mowing the lawn and washing the car.

Mom was in the kitchen preparing breakfast. Mark said, "Mom, I can not do anything to help Dad. They keep telling me I am too small. 'You will grow taller as you get older.'" Mark said, "Who am I?"

Mom said, "You are my precious little boy, and you are the apple of God's eye. This is what the Bible says in Psalm 17:8."

Mark started playing with his trucks and cars on the living room floor.

He played for a little while and then got up and went to get his favorite blocks. Mark started looking and playing with the blocks. As he picked up the blocks, he looked at each picture on the blocks. B is for bear, F is for fish, J is for juice. He picked up the letter A, and A is for apple. He then said, "Apple of God's eye."

D
A

He continued to look and play with the blocks. B is for bear, C is for cat, D is for dog, E is for egg.

Then he went back to the block, which had the letter A and said again, "A is for apple."

Again he said, "Apple of God's eye, what does this mean?"

Mom had washed some towels and was busy folding them. Mark sits next to her with his block in his hand.

He said A is for apple. Mom said, "Yes, that is right."

"Mom, how can I be the apple of God's eye? Can I get in His eyes? Will He be able to see? You know I am big, eyes are little. Can I fit in His eyes?"

"No, baby, that is not what the Bible is saying. The Bible is saying: The Lord is always watching over you, protecting, and guiding you in the right way to go. No matter what you go through as you grow, God will always be with you."

Mom said, "I know you think you are small. But God uses the most unlikely people to get His work done on the earth. Let me tell you a story in the Bible about a little boy named David. This story is found in 1 Samuel, chapter 16."

"Now David was a little boy. He was not strong and big like his brothers. He was the youngest of seven boys; their father's name was Jesse. One special thing about David is that he knew and trusted in the Lord. One day God told Samuel to go to Jesse's house and anoint one of his sons because he would become king over Israel.

Samuel meets with Jesse and his sons. Samuel was looking at how strong and tall they were, but God did not choose them. He told Samuel not to look at their looks and how tall they were because he did not want them.

Samuel said, 'Are these all your sons?' Jesse told him that he had another son, but he kept the sheep. Samuel said to send for him.

When David passed by Samuel, the oil started flowing, for this is a sign from God that David is the chosen one to be king. Samuel anointed David to be king. He was between the age of ten and fifteen. So, you see God can use you if you are young and small, only trust in Him."

At bedtime, Mark said his prayers: "Thank You, God, for I am the apple of Your eye. I am young and little in size, You love me, and You can use me. Thank You for protecting, leading, and guiding me every day. I love You, Lord. Thank You for my family."

Who Am I? Book Two Scriptures

"Keep me [in Your affectionate care protect me] as the apple of Your eye; Hide me in the [protective] shadow of Your wings" (Psalm 17:8, AMP).

"So Jessie sent *word* and brought him in. Now he had a ruddy complexion, with beautiful eyes and a handsome appearance. The Lord said [to Samuel], 'Arise, anoint him; for this is he'" (1 Samuel 16:12, AMP).